music

London Borough of Hounslow

Feltham Library
The Centre
Feltham TW13 4GU

020 8890 3506

Please telephone for
complete opening times.

Hounslow Library Services

This item should be returned or renewed by the latest date shown. If
it is not required by another reader, you may renew it in person or by
telephone (twice only). Please quote your library card number. A charge
will be made for items returned or renewed after that date due.

16-9-11			
			P10-L-2138

CD at
Back of
Book

BAR
CODE
REFERS
TO
BOOK +
CD

play guitar with...

kaiser chiefs

Wise Publications
part of The Music Sales Group
London / New York / Paris / Sydney / Copenhagen / Berlin / Madrid / Tokyo

Published by
Wise Publications
14-15 Berners Street, London W1T 3LJ, UK.

Exclusive Distributors:
Music Sales Limited
Distribution Centre, Newmarket Road,
Bury St Edmunds, Suffolk IP33 3YB, UK.

Music Sales Pty Limited
120 Rothschild Avenue,
Rosebery, NSW 2018, Australia.

Order No. AM991617
ISBN 978-1-84772-239-3
This book © Copyright 2007 Wise Publications,
a division of Music Sales Limited.

Compiled by Nick Crispin.
Music arranged by Arthur Dick.
Edited by Tom Farncombe.
Music processed by Paul Ewers Music Design.

All guitars by Arthur Dick.
Bass by Paul Townsend.
Drums by Brett Morgan.
Keyboards by Jonas Persson and Arthur Dick.
CD recorded, mixed and mastered by Jonas Persson.

Printed in the EU.

www.musicsales.com

guitar tablature explained

Guitar music can be notated in three different ways: on a musical stave, in tablature, and in rhythm slashes.

RHYTHM SLASHES: are written above the stave. Strum chords in the rhythm indicated. Round noteheads indicate single notes.

THE MUSICAL STAVE: shows pitches and rhythms and is divided by lines into bars. Pitches are named after the first seven letters of the alphabet.

TABLATURE: graphically represents the guitar fingerboard. Each horizontal line represents a string, and each number represents a fret.

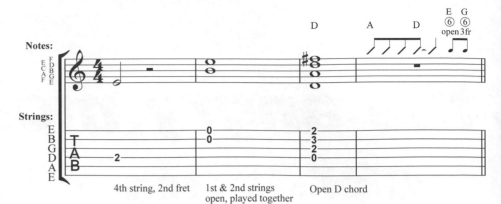

4th string, 2nd fret   1st & 2nd strings open, played together   Open D chord

definitions for special guitar notation

SEMI-TONE BEND: Strike the note and bend up a semi-tone (½ step).

WHOLE-TONE BEND: Strike the note and bend up a whole-tone (full step).

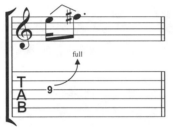

GRACE NOTE BEND: Strike the note and bend as indicated. Play the first note as quickly as possible.

QUARTER-TONE BEND: Strike the note and bend up a ¼ step

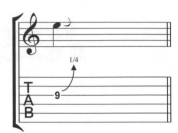

BEND & RELEASE: Strike the note and bend up as indicated, then release back to the original note.

COMPOUND BEND & RELEASE: Strike the note and bend up and down in the rhythm indicated.

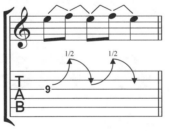

PRE-BEND: Bend the note as indicated, then strike it.

PRE-BEND & RELEASE: Bend the note as indicated. Strike it and release the note back to the original pitch.

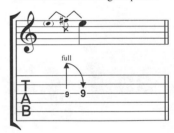

HAMMER-ON: Strike the first note with one finger, then sound the second note (on the same string) with another finger by fretting it without picking.

PULL-OFF: Place both fingers on the note to be sounded, strike the first note and without picking, pull the finger off to sound the second note.

LEGATO SLIDE (GLISS): Strike the first note and then slide the same fret-hand finger up or down to the second note. The second note is not struck.

MUFFLED STRINGS: A percussive sound is produced by laying the first hand across the string(s) without depressing, and striking them with the pick hand.

NATURAL HARMONIC: Strike the note while the fret-hand lightly touches the string directly over the fret indicated.

PICK SCRAPE: The edge of the pick is rubbed down (or up) the string, producing a scratchy sound.

PALM MUTING: The note is partially muted by the pick hand lightly touching the string(s) just before the bridge.

SHIFT SLIDE (GLISS & RESTRIKE) Same as legato slide, except the second note is struck.

SLAP HARMONIC: The note is fretted normally and a harmonic is produced by 'slapping' or tapping the fret indicated in brackets (which will be twelve frets higher than the fretted note.)

TAPPING: Hammer ('tap') the fret indicated with the pick-hand index or middle finger and pull-off to the note fretted by the fret hand.

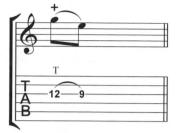

PINCH HARMONIC: The note is fretted normally and a harmonic is produced by adding the edge of the thumb or the tip of the index finger of the pick hand to the normal pick attack.

ARTIFICIAL HARMONIC: The note fretted normally and a harmonic is produced by gently resting the pick hand's index finger directly above the indicated fret (in brackets) while plucking the appropriate string.

TRILL: Very rapidly alternate between the notes indicated by continuously hammering-on and pulling-off.

RAKE: Drag the pick across the strings with a single motion.

TREMOLO PICKING: The note is picked as rapidly and continously as possible.

ARPEGGIATE: Play the notes of the chord indicated by quickly rolling them from bottom to top.

SWEEP PICKING: Rhythmic downstroke and/or upstroke motion across the strings.

VIBRATO DIVE BAR AND RETURN: The pitch of the note or chord is dropped a specific number of steps (in rhythm) then returned to the original pitch.

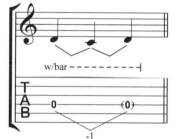

VIBRATO BAR SCOOP: Depress the bar just before striking the note, then quickly release the bar.

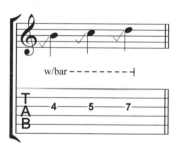

VIBRATO BAR DIP: Strike the note and then immediately drop a specific number of steps, then release back to the original pitch.

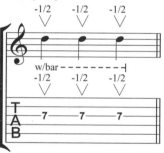

additional musical definitions

(accent)	Accentuate note (play it louder)	
(accent)	Accentuate note with greater intensity	
(staccato)	Shorten time value of note	
⊓	Downstroke	
V	Upstroke	

D.S. al Coda — Go back to the sign (𝄋), then play until the bar marked **To Coda** ⊕ then skip to the section marked ⊕ **Coda**

D.C. al Fine — Go back to the beginning of the song and play until the bar marked **Fine.**

tacet — Instrument is silent (drops out).

Repeat bars between signs

1. 2. — When a repeat section has different endings, play the first ending only the first time and the second ending only the second time.

NOTE: Tablature numbers in brackets mean:
1. The note is sustained, but a new articulation (such as hammer-on or slide) begins
2. A note may be fretted but not necessarily played.

5

the angry mob

Words & Music by
Nicholas Hodgson, Richard Wilson, Andrew White,
James Rix & Nicholas Baines

Full performance demo: CD track 1
Backing only: CD track 9

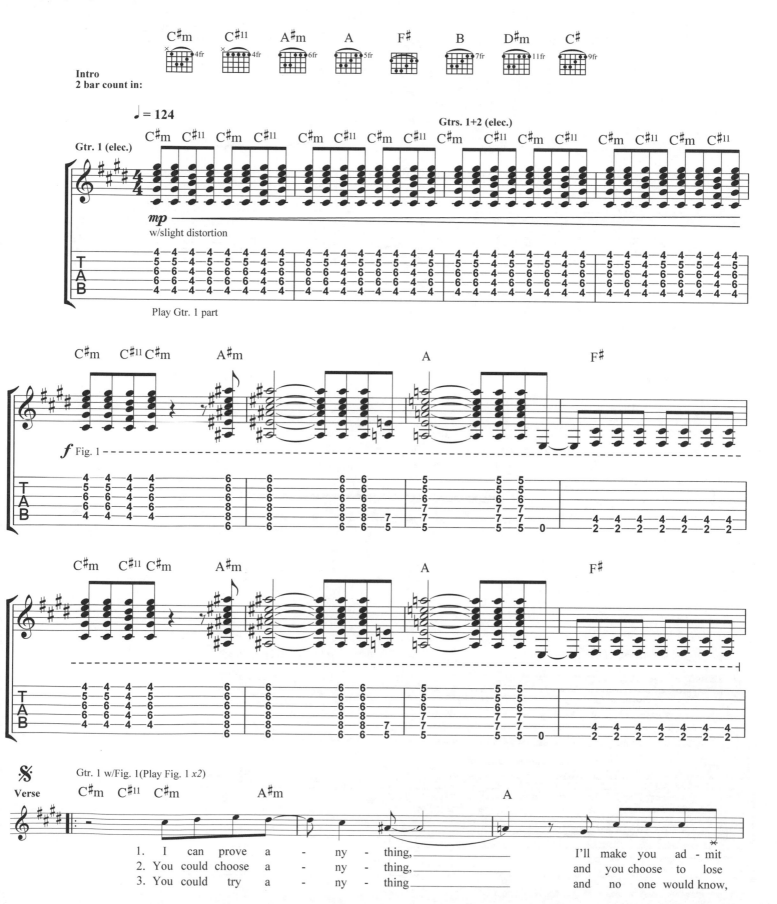

7

So here we go with the let - ter:___ "Well can you fix it for me,___
So here we go with the let - ter:___ "Oh can you fix it for me,___

___ be - cause we need en - ter - tain - ment ___
___ for twen - ty four hour ___ drink - ing ___

to keep us all off the streets."___ So to - night you'll___ sleep
to keep us all off the streets."___ So to - night you'll___ sleep

Gtr. 2 plays chord box positions

To Coda ✛   *D.S. al Coda*

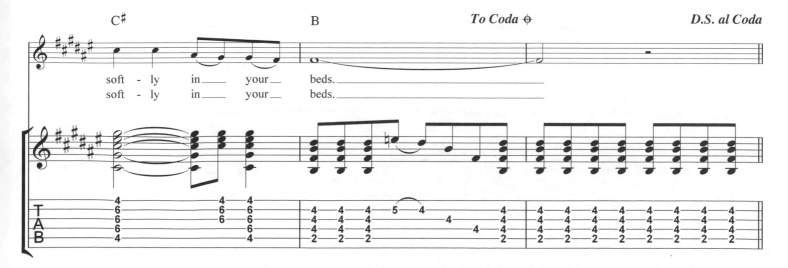

soft - ly in___ your___ beds.___
soft - ly in___ your___ beds.___

caroline, yes

**Words & Music by
Nicholas Hodgson, Richard Wilson, Andrew White,
James Rix & Nicholas Baines**

Full performance demo: CD track 2
Backing only: CD track 10

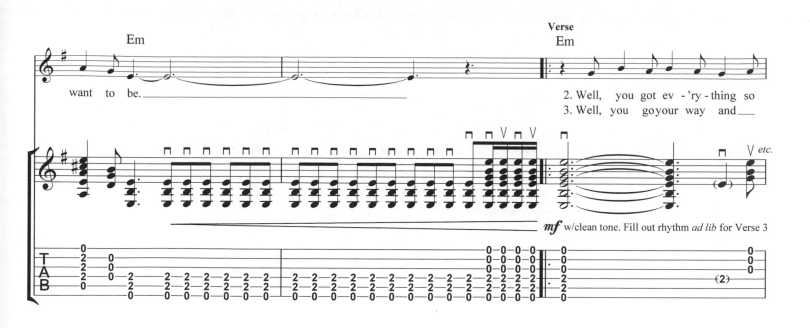

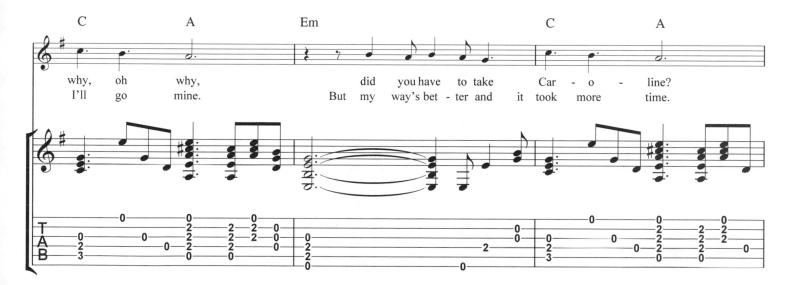

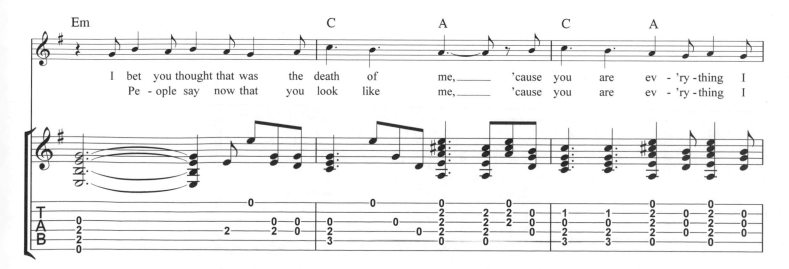

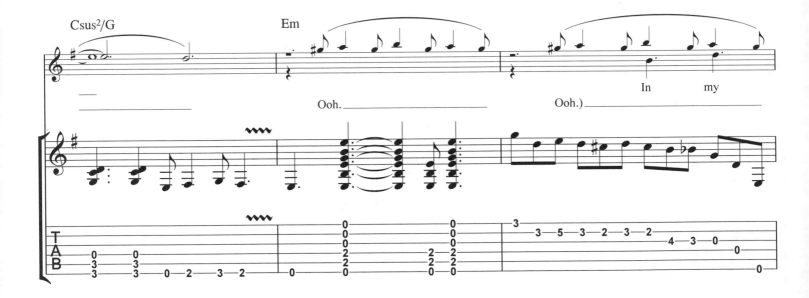

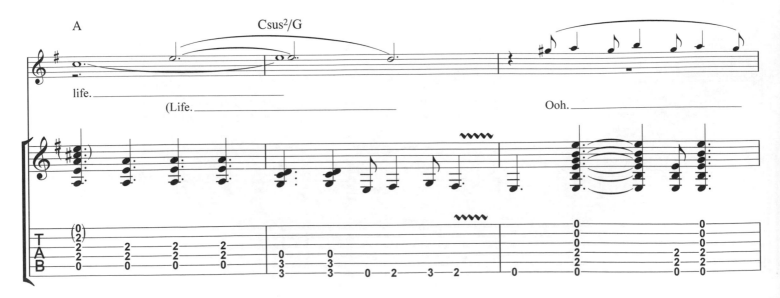

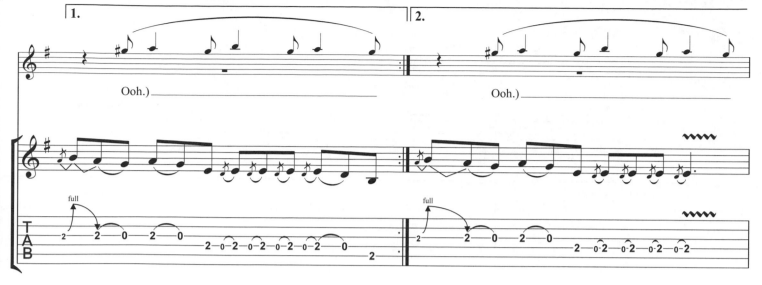

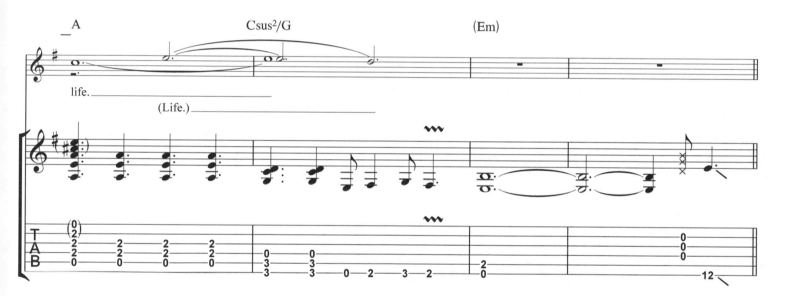

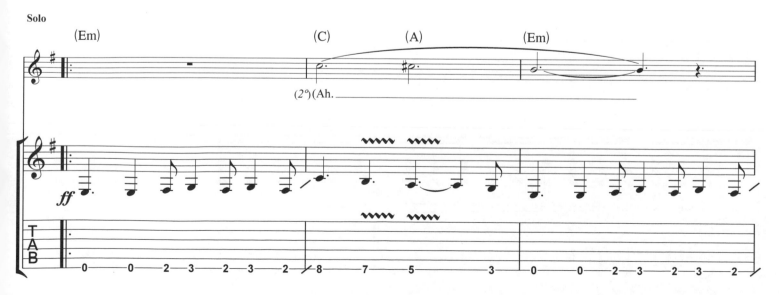

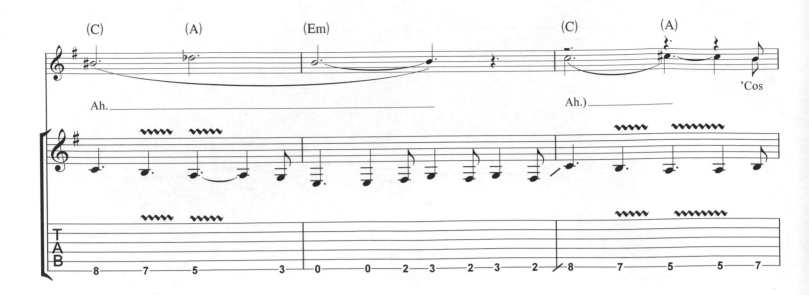

'Cos

Ah._____   Ah.)_____

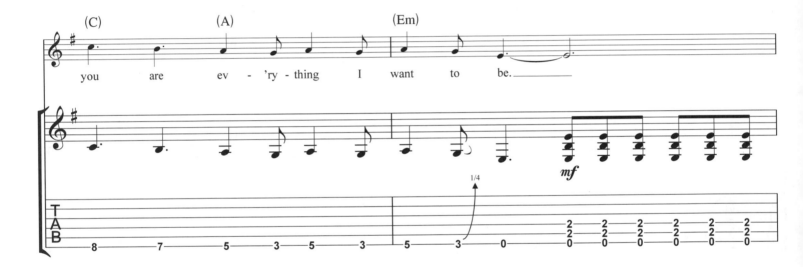

you are ev - 'ry - thing   I   want   to   be._____

mf

D.S. al Coda
(No Repeat)

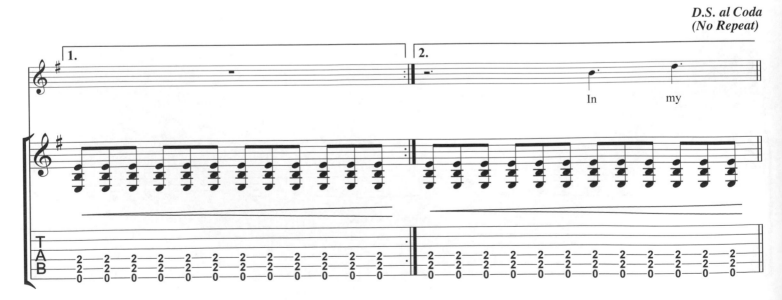

In   my

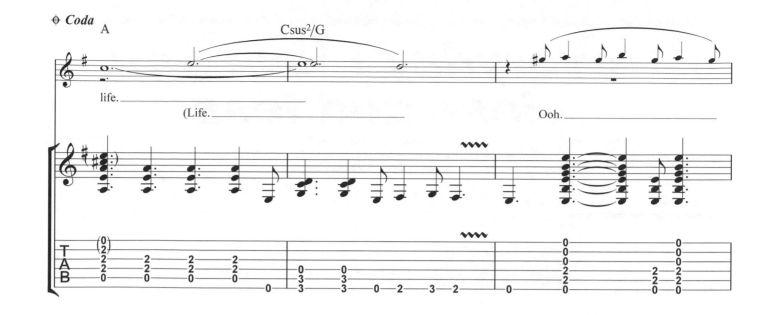

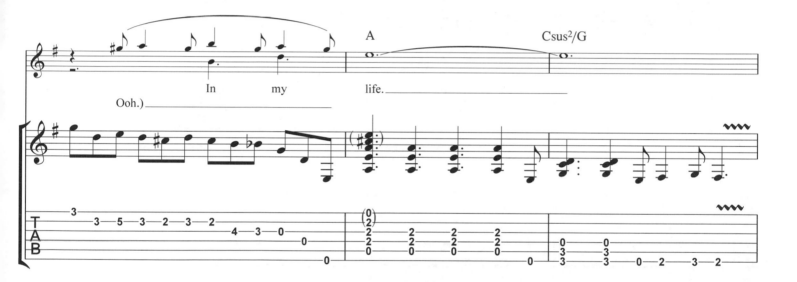

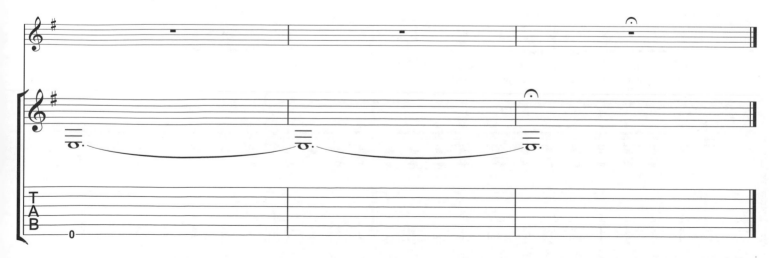

everyday i love you less and less

Words & Music by
Nicholas Hodgson, Richard Wilson, Andrew White,
James Rix & Nicholas Baines

Full performance demo: CD track 3
Backing only: CD track 11

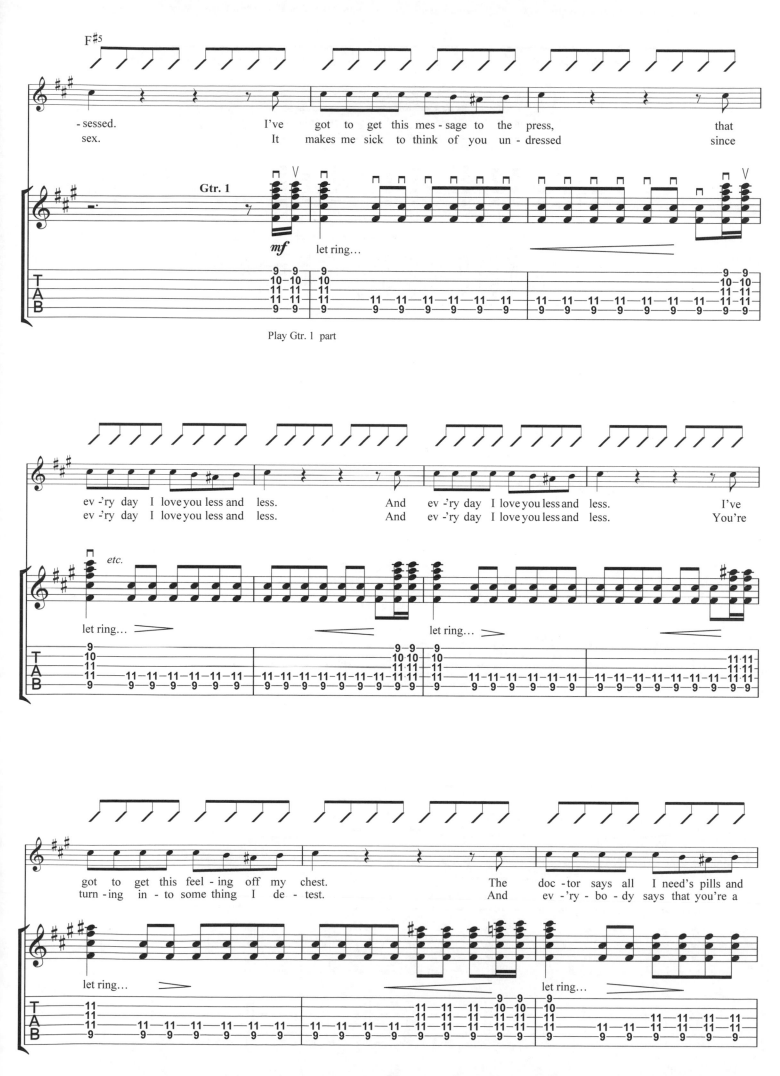

Play Gtr. 1 part

19

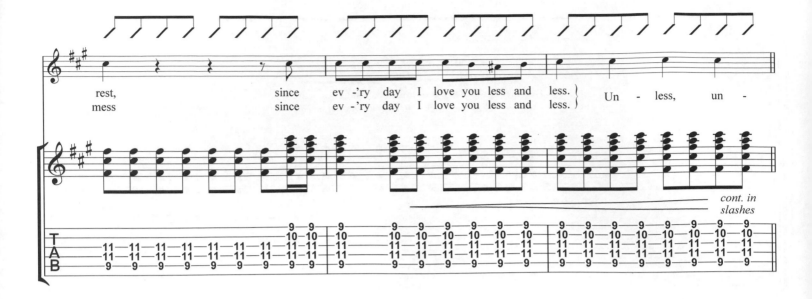

rest,
mess
since ev -'ry day I love you less and less.
since ev -'ry day I love you less and less.
Un - less, un -

cont. in slashes

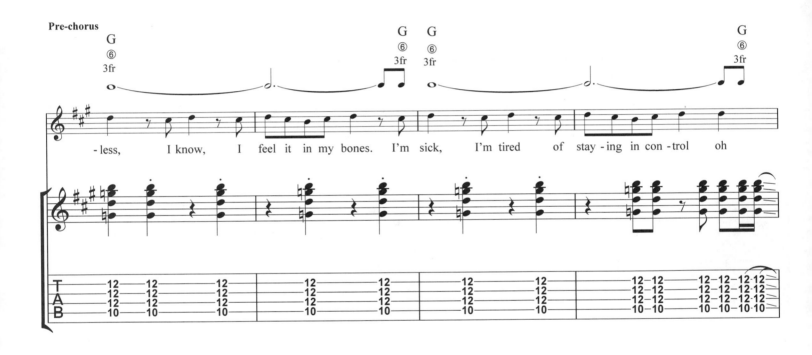

Pre-chorus

G
⑥
3fr

G
⑥
3fr

G
⑥
3fr

G
⑥
3fr

- less, I know, I feel it in my bones. I'm sick, I'm tired of stay -ing in con -trol oh

F#
⑥
2fr

F#
⑥
2fr

F#
⑥
2fr

F#
⑥
2fr

yes. I feel a rat up -on a wheel, I've got to know what's not and what is real. Oh

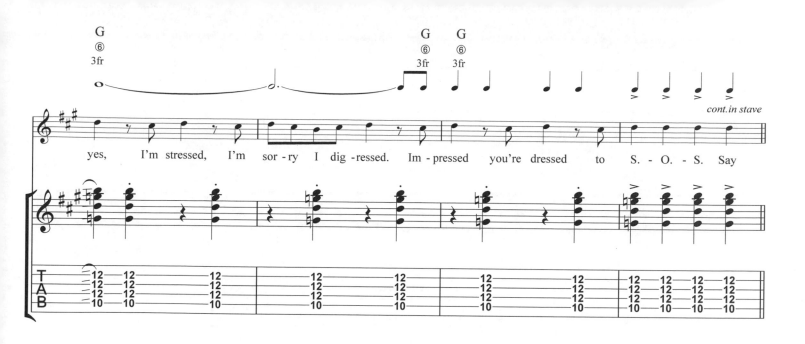

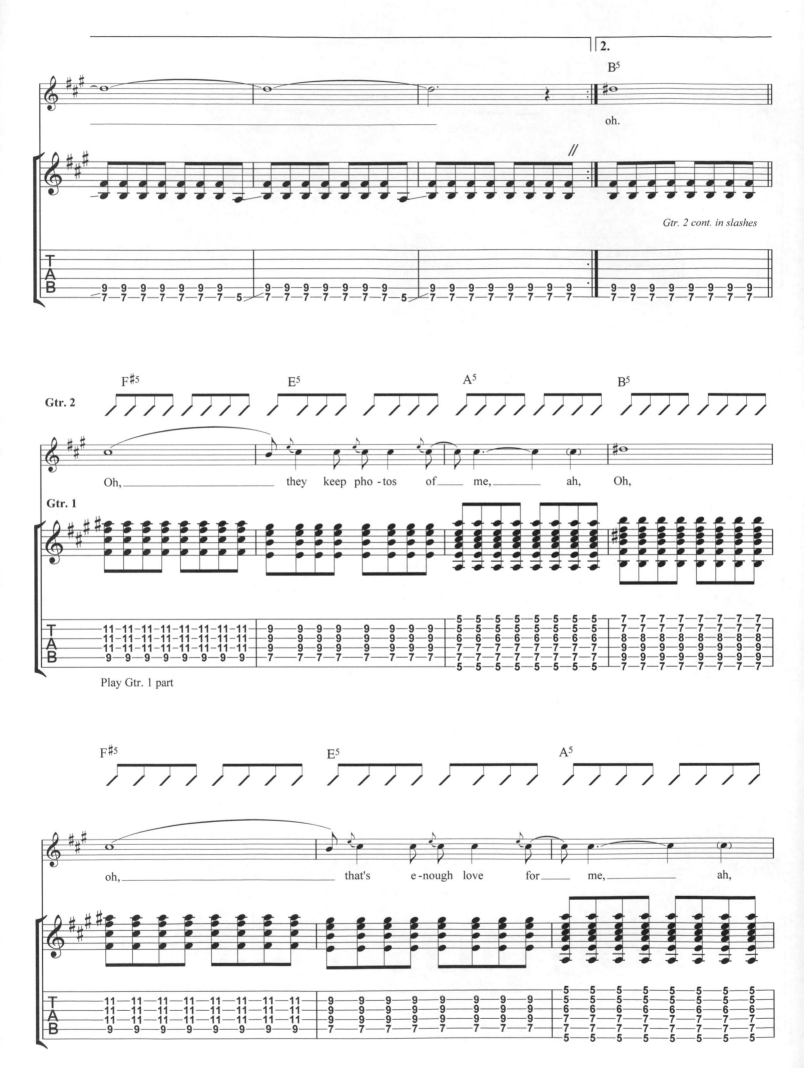

Gtr. 2 cont. in slashes

Gtr. 2

Oh, _____ they keep pho -tos of ___ me, _____ ah, Oh,

Gtr. 1

Play Gtr. 1 part

oh, _____ that's e -nough love for ___ me, _____ ah,

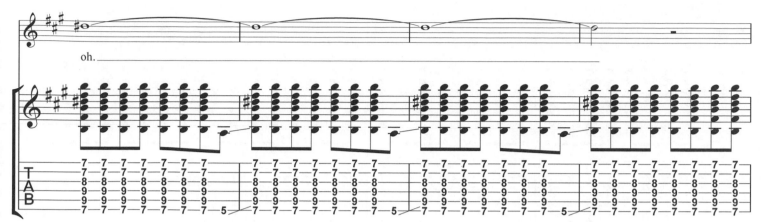

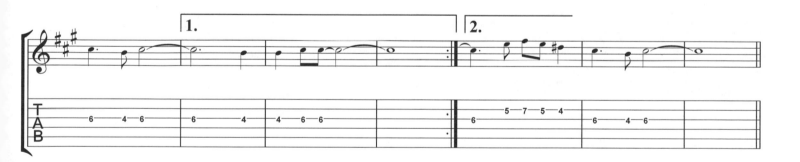

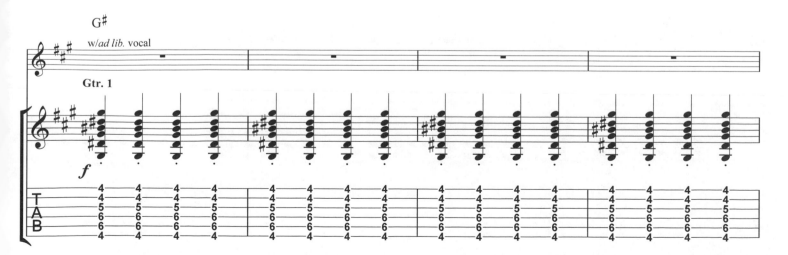

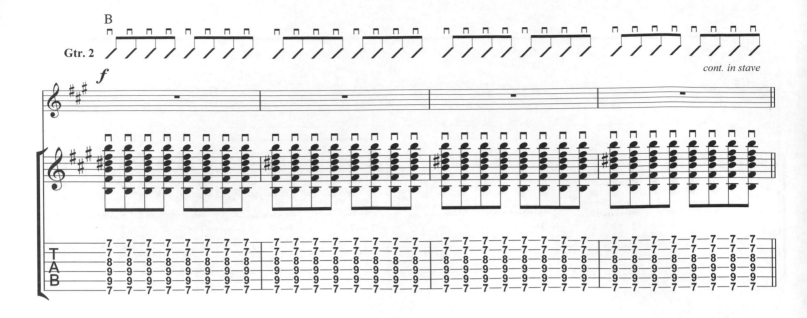

Outro Chorus

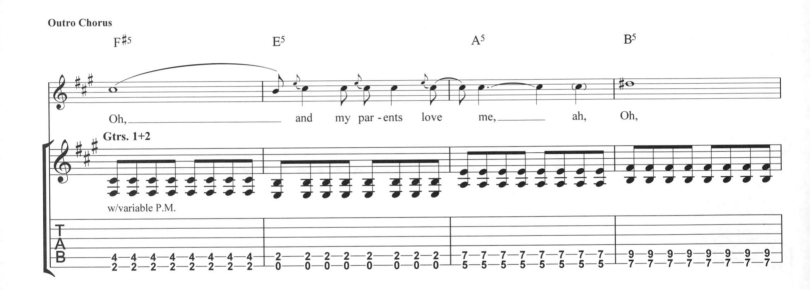

Oh,_____ and my par-ents love me,_____ ah, Oh,

w/variable P.M.

oh,_____ and my girl-friend loves me,_____ ah, oh.

Gtr. 2 cont. in slashes

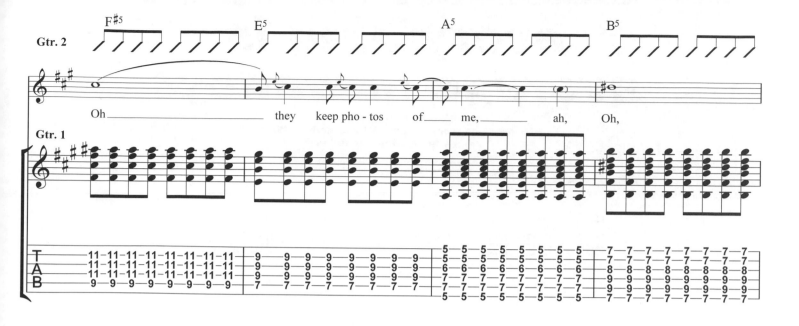

Oh _____ they keep pho - tos of ____ me, _____ ah, Oh,

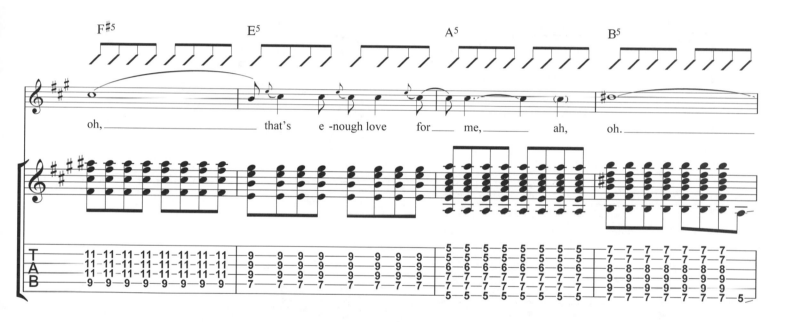

oh, _____ that's e - nough love for ____ me, _____ ah, oh. _____

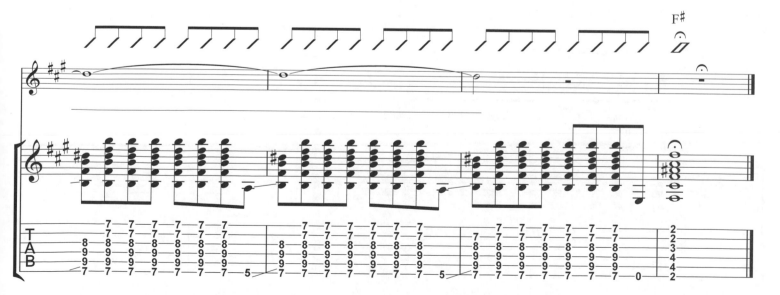

everything is
average nowadays

Words & Music by
Nicholas Hodgson, Richard Wilson, Andrew White,
James Rix & Nicholas Baines

Full performance demo: CD track 4
Backing only: CD track 12

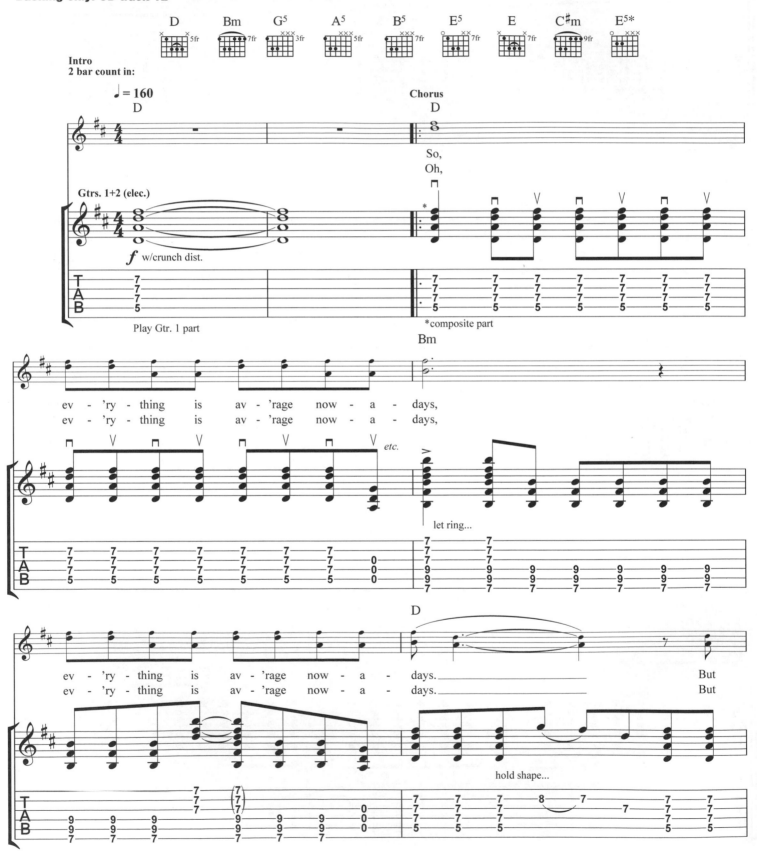

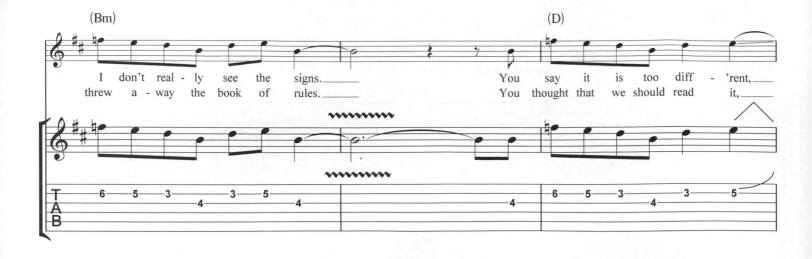

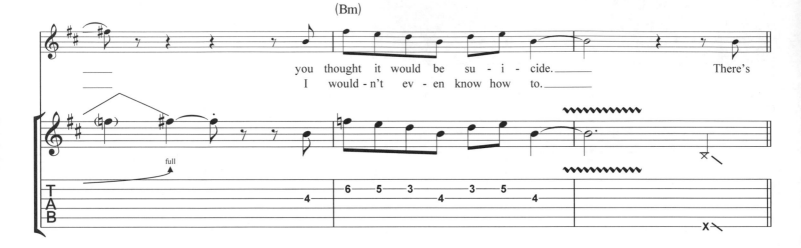

Pre-chorus

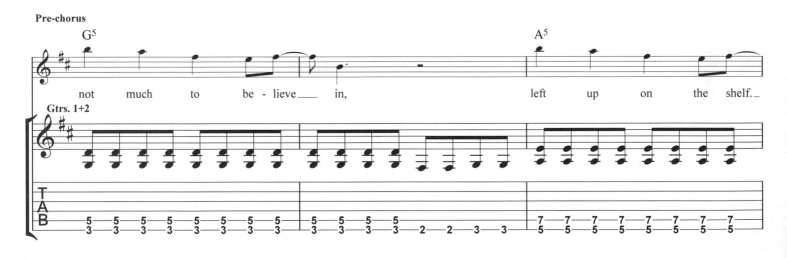

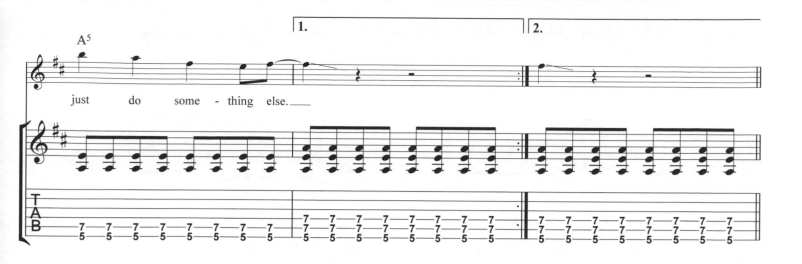

just do some - thing else.____

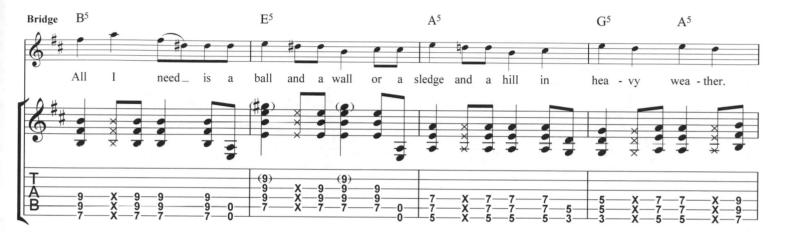

Bridge

All I need__ is a ball and a wall or a sledge and a hill in hea - vy wea - ther.

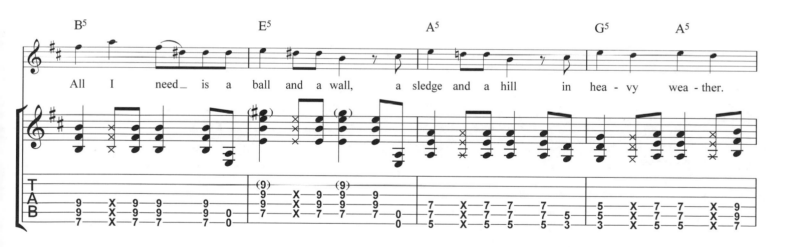

All I need__ is a ball and a wall, a sledge and a hill in hea - vy wea - ther.

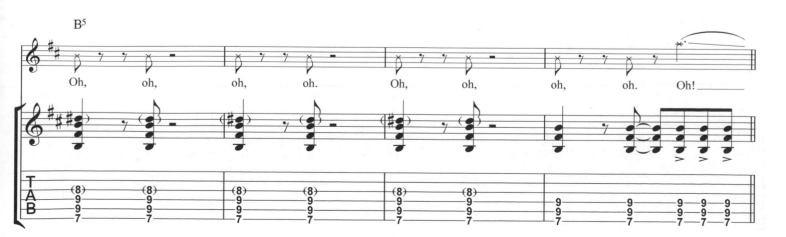

Oh, oh, oh, oh. Oh, oh, oh, oh. Oh!____

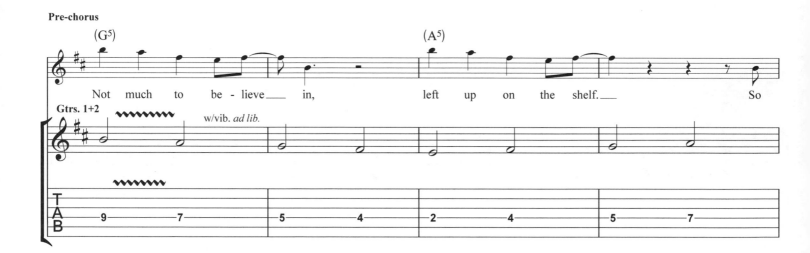

Not much to be-lieve___ in, left up on the shelf.___ So

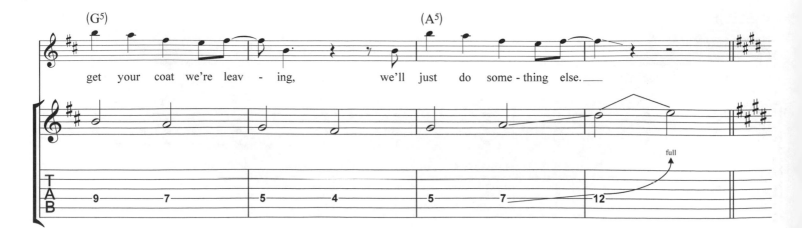

get your coat we're leav - ing, we'll just do some-thing else.___

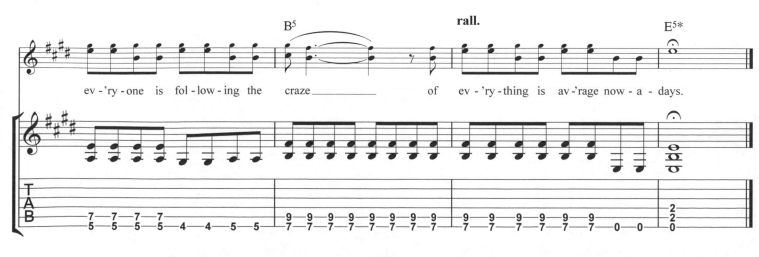

i predict a riot

Words & Music by
Nicholas Hodgson, Richard Wilson, Andrew White,
James Rix & Nicholas Baines

Full performance demo: CD track 5
Backing only: CD track 13

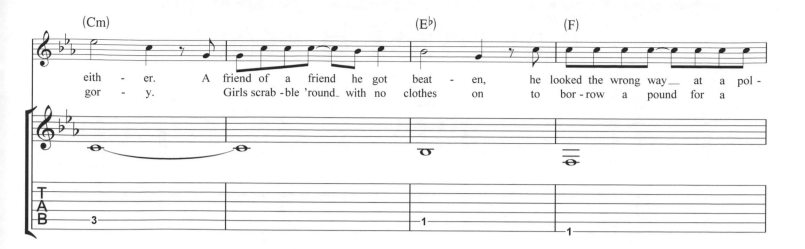

eith - er. A friend of a friend he got beat - en, he looked the wrong way __ at a pol -
gor - y. Girls scrab -ble 'round_ with no clothes on to bor -row a pound for a

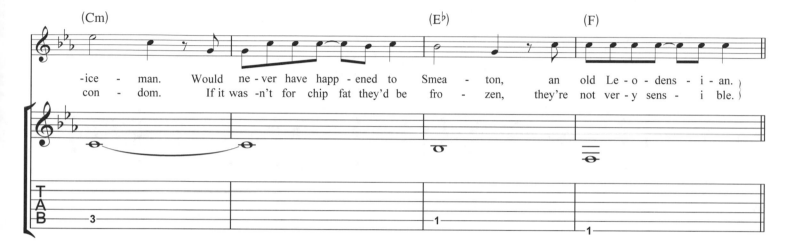

-ice - man. Would ne -ver have happ -ened to Smea -ton, an old Le -o -dens -i -an.
con - dom. If it was -n't for chip fat they'd be fro -zen, they're not ver -y sens -i -ble.

Pre-chorus

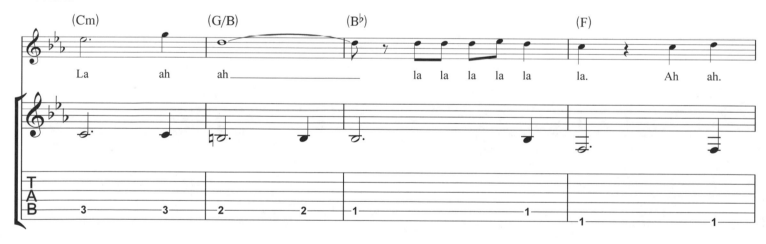

La ah ah_____ la la la la la la. Ah ah.

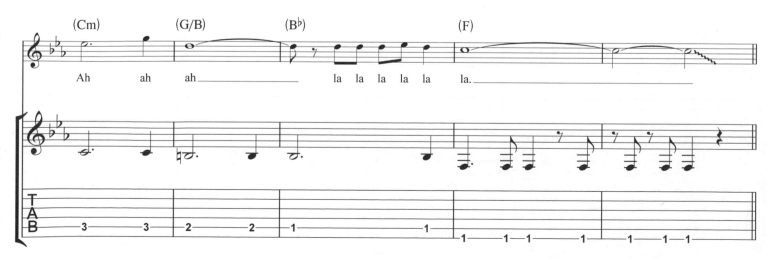

Ah ah ah_____ la la la la la la._____

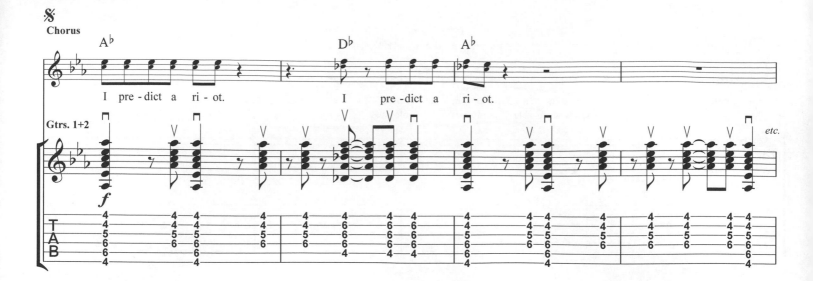

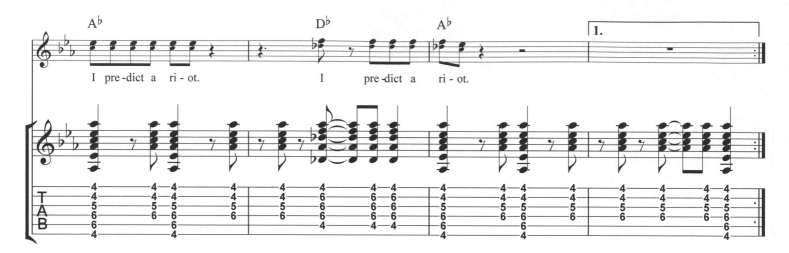

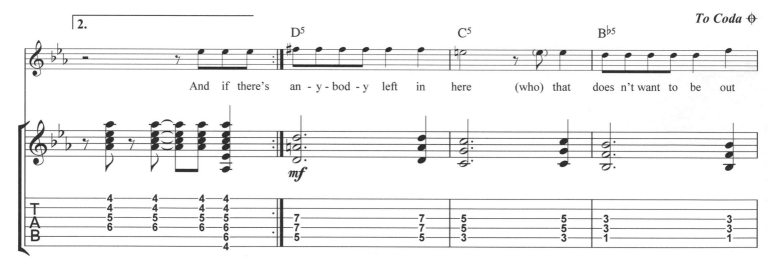

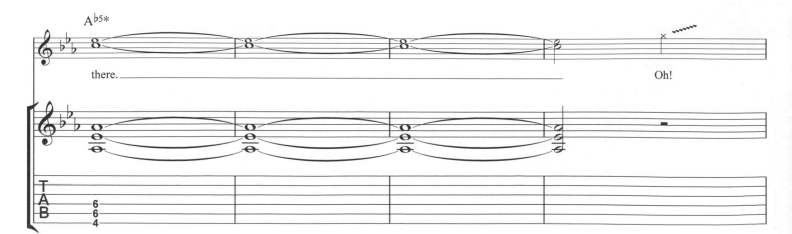

Pre-chorus

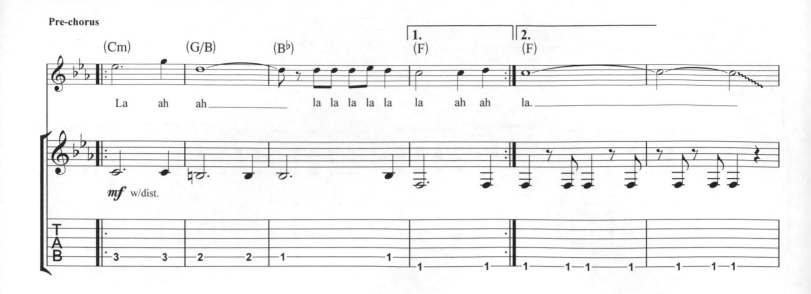

La   ah   ah_____   la la la la la la ah ah la._____

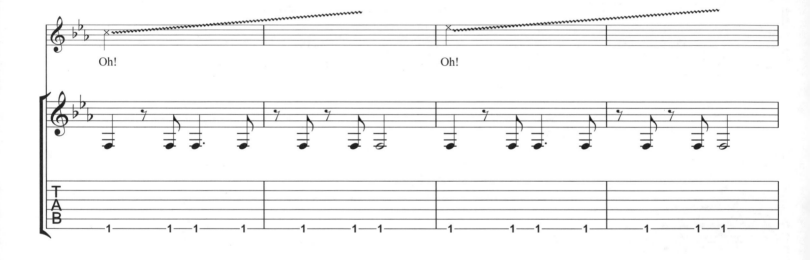

Oh!   Oh!

D.S. al Coda   ⊕ ***Coda***

Oh!

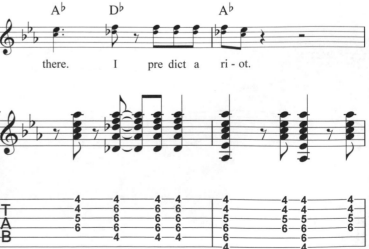

there.   I   pre dict a ri - ot.

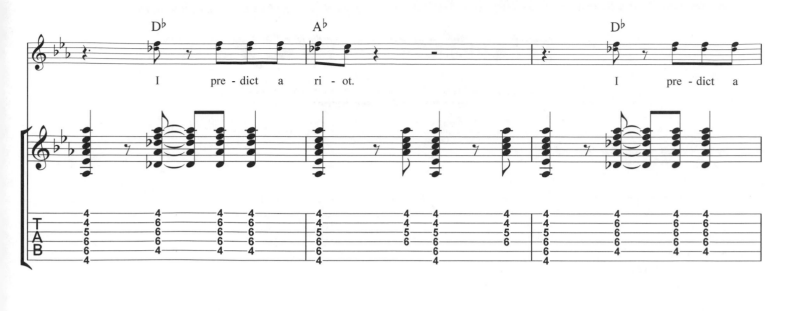

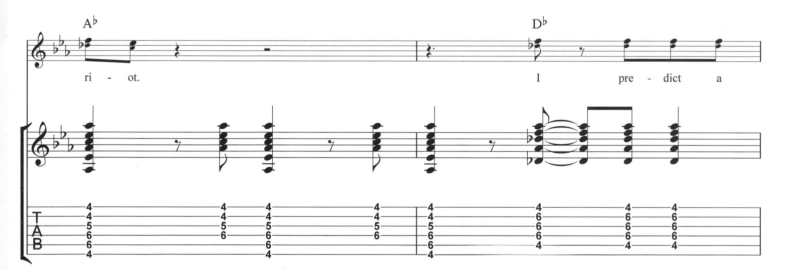

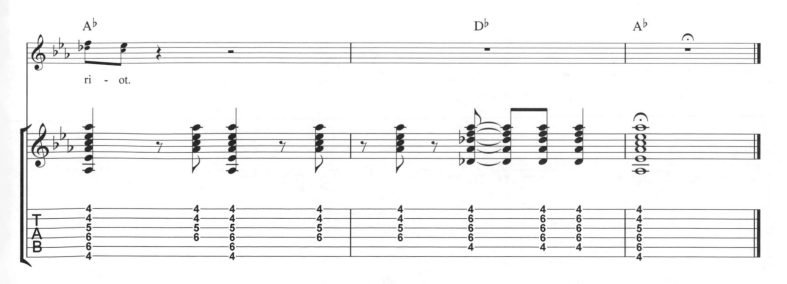

modern way

Words & Music by
Nicholas Hodgson, Richard Wilson, Andrew White,
James Rix & Nicholas Baines

Full performance demo: CD track 6
Backing only: CD track 14

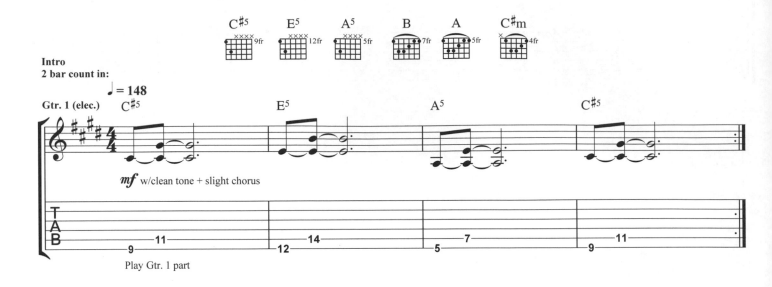

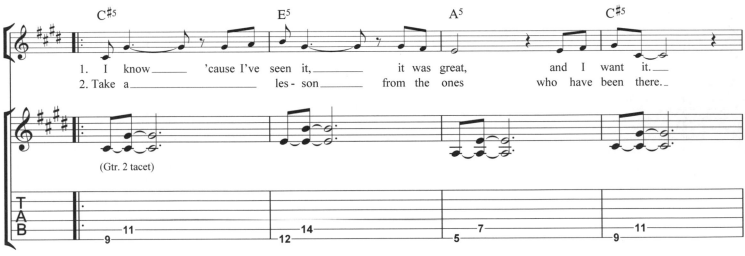

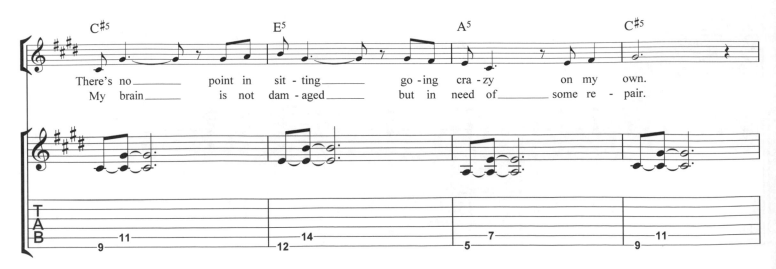

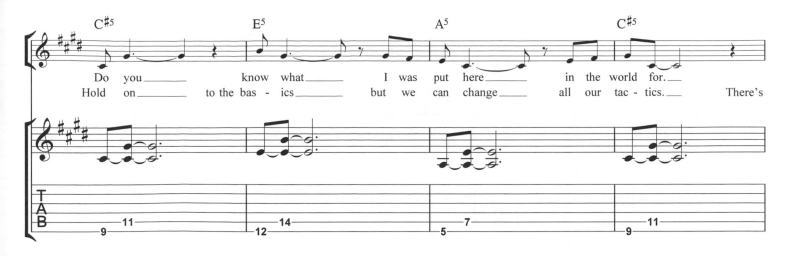

C#5   E5   A5   C#5

Do you_____ know what_____ I was put here_____ in the world for._____ There's
Hold on_____ to the bas - ics_____ but we can change_____ all our tac - tics._____

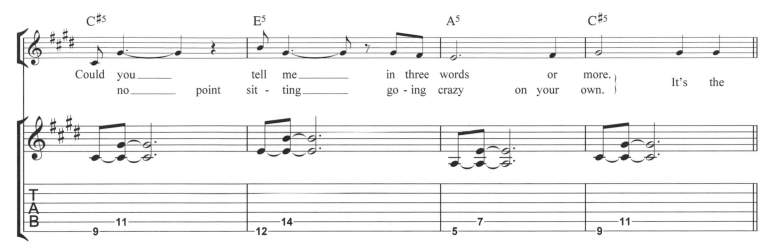

C#5   E5   A5   C#5

Could you_____ tell me_____ in three words or more._____ It's the
no_____ point sit - ting_____ go - ing crazy on your own._____

Pre-Chorus

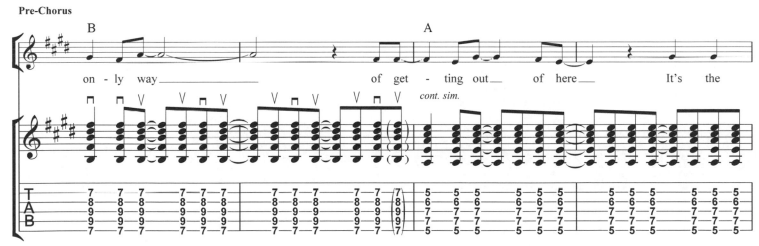

B   A

on - ly way_____ of get - ting out_____ of here_____ It's the

cont. sim.

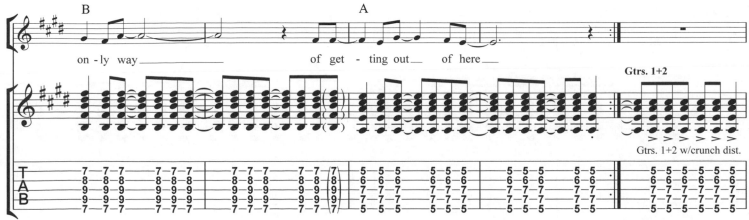

B   A

on - ly way_____ of get - ting out_____ of here_____

Gtrs. 1+2

Gtrs. 1+2 w/crunch dist.

*composite part

Chorus

This is the mod-ern way ___ of fak-ing it ev-'ry day,

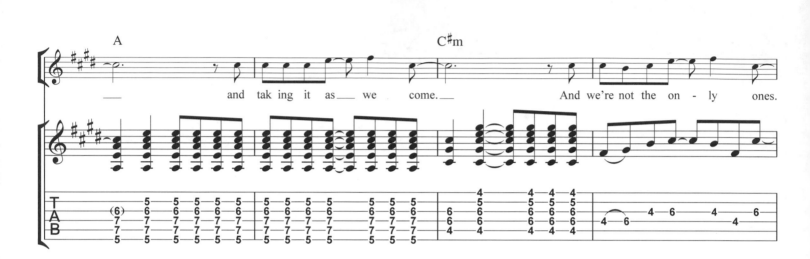

___ and tak-ing it as ___ we come. ___ And we're not the on-ly ones.

___ Is that what we used ___ to say? ___ This is the mod-ern way

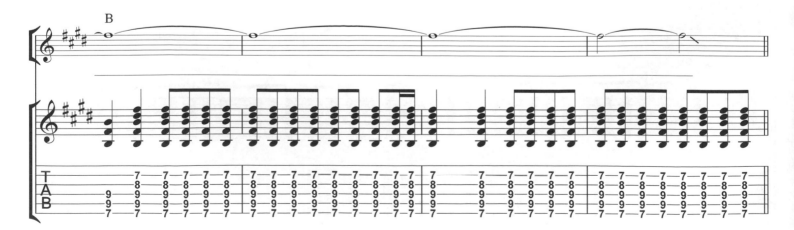

Verse

C#5 E5 A5 C#5

Vocal tacet 1°

3. I know_____ where I'm go-ing_____ and that we are_____ in the know - ing. And

mf w/clean tone + slight chorus

C#5 E5 A5 **1.** C#5 **2.** C#5

I will_____ stop at no - thing_____ just to get what I want. It's the

Pre-Chorus

B A

on - ly way_____ of get - ting out__ of here_____ It's the

cont. sim.

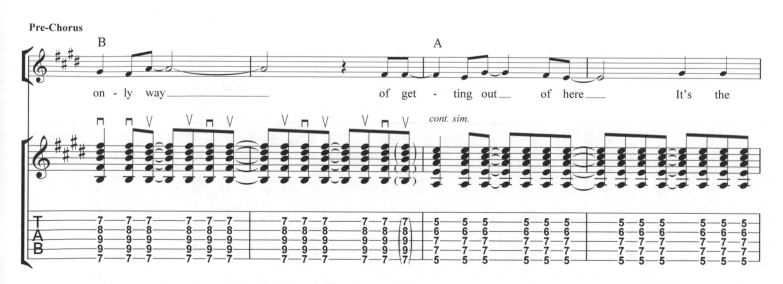

on - ly way_____ of get - ting out__ of here__

Chorus

This is the mod - ern way__ of fak - ing it ev - 'ry day,

hold shape....

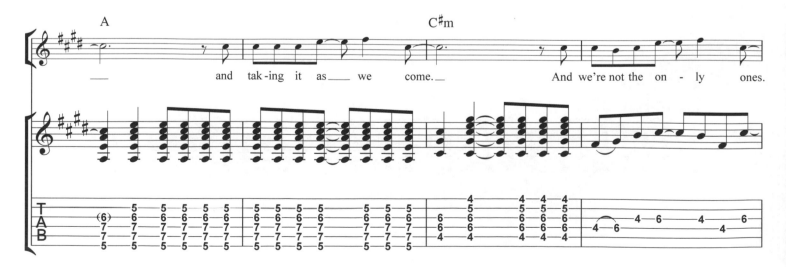

___ and tak - ing it as__ we come.__ And we're not the on - ly ones.

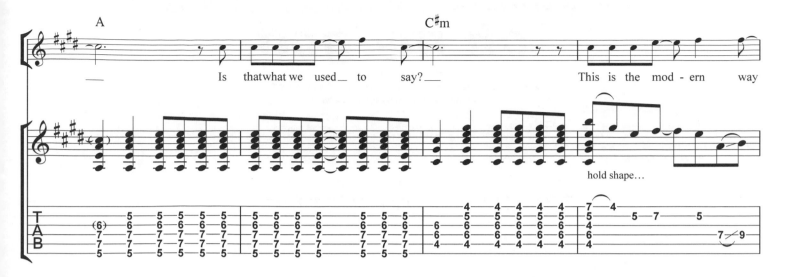

Is that what we used to say? This is the mod-ern way

hold shape…

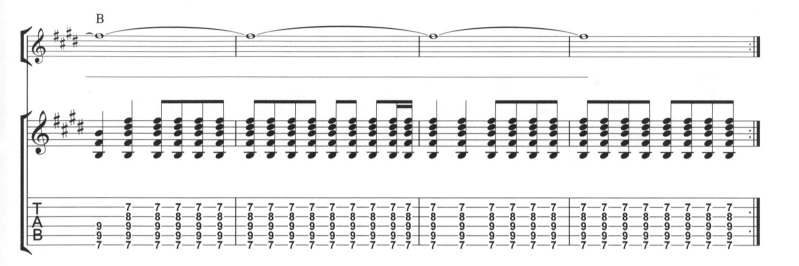

Outro

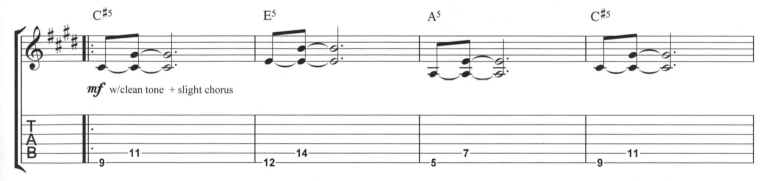

mf w/clean tone + slight chorus

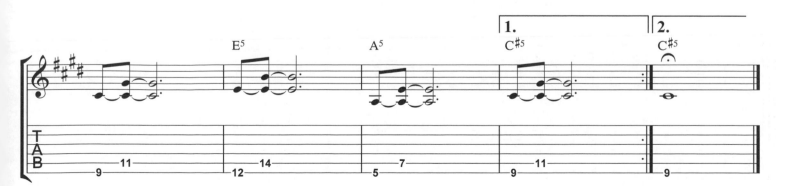

oh my god

Words & Music by
Nicholas Hodgson, Richard Wilson, Andrew White,
James Rix & Nicholas Baines

Full performance demo: CD track 7
Backing only: CD track 15

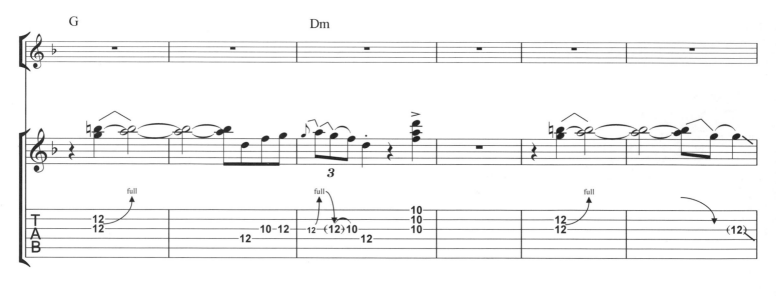

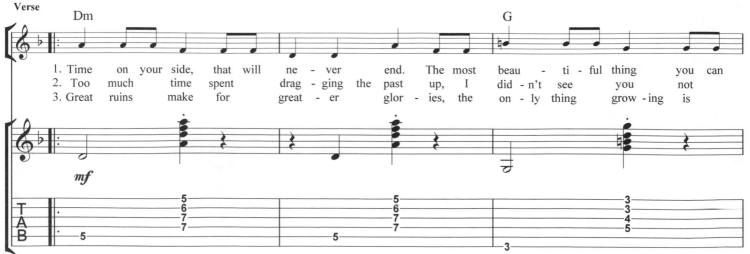

1. Time on your side, that will ne-ver end. The most beau-ti-ful thing you can
2. Too much time spent drag-ging the past up, I did-n't see you not
3. Great ruins make for great-er glor-ies, the on-ly thing grow-ing is

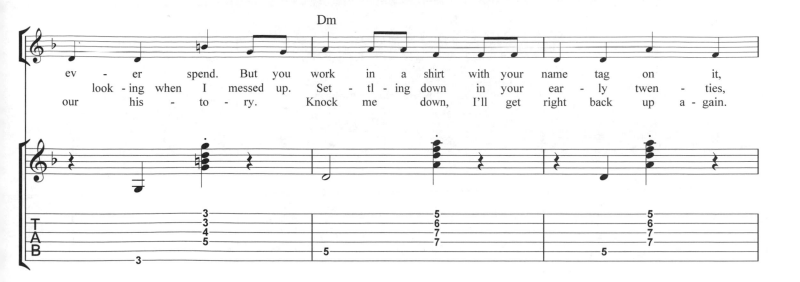

ev - er spend. But you work in a shirt with your name tag on it,
look - ing when I messed up. Set - tl - ing down in your ear - ly twen - ties,
our his - to - ry. Knock me down, I'll get right back up a - gain.

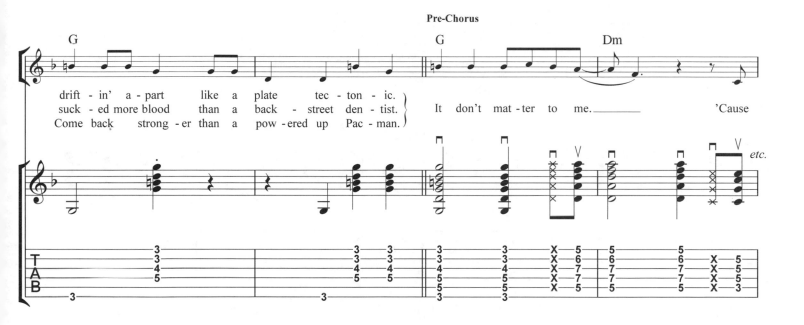

drift - in' a - part like a plate tec - ton - ic.
suck - ed more blood than a back - street den - tist.
Come back strong - er than a pow - ered up Pac - man.

It don't mat - ter to me._____ 'Cause

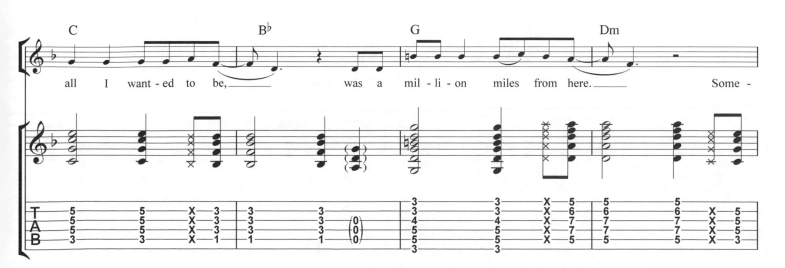

all I want - ed to be,_____ was a mil - li - on miles from here._____ Some -

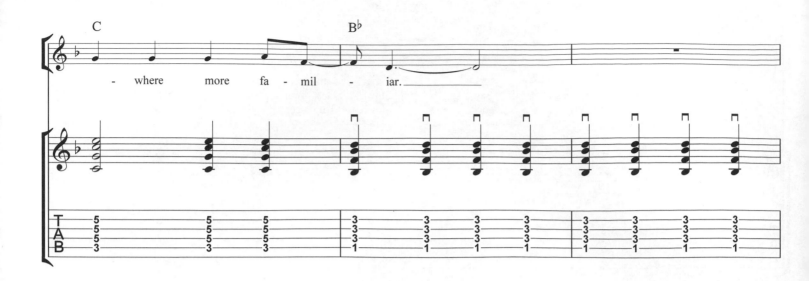

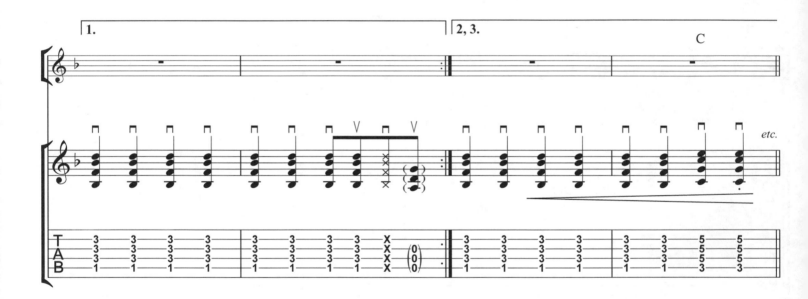

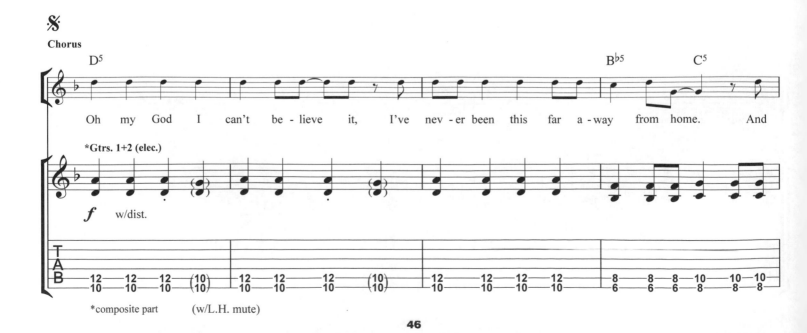

oh my God I can't be - lieve it, I've nev - er been this far a - way from home. And

To Coda ⊕

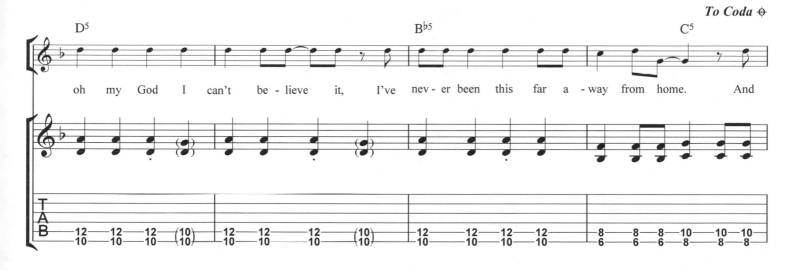

oh my God I can't be - lieve it, I've nev - er been this far a - way from home. And

1.　　　　　**2.**

oh my God I can't be - lieve it, I've nev - er been this far a - way from home.　　way from home.

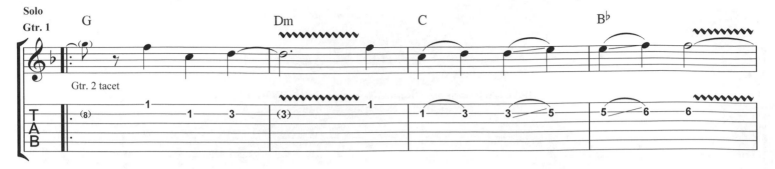

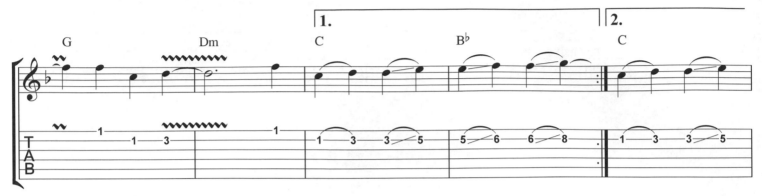

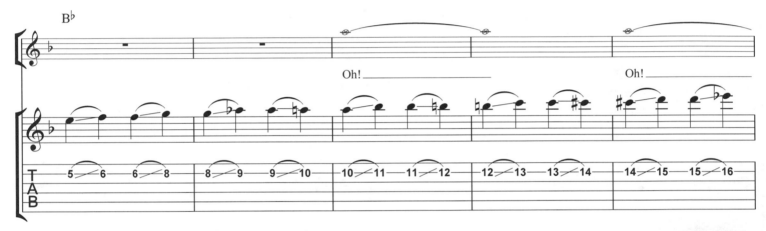

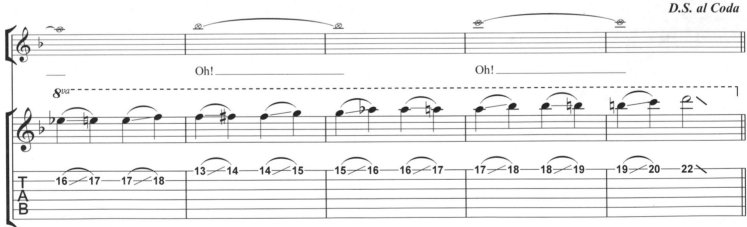

oh my God I can't be-lieve it, I've nev-er been this far a-way from home.

ruby

Words & Music by
Nicholas Hodgson, Richard Wilson, Andrew White,
James Rix & Nicholas Baines

Full performance demo: CD track 8
Backing only: CD track 16

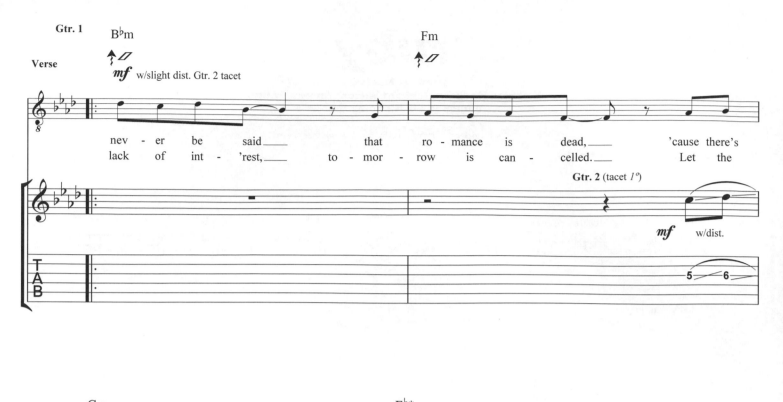

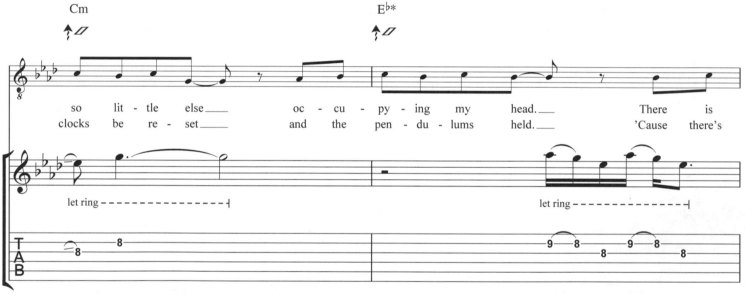

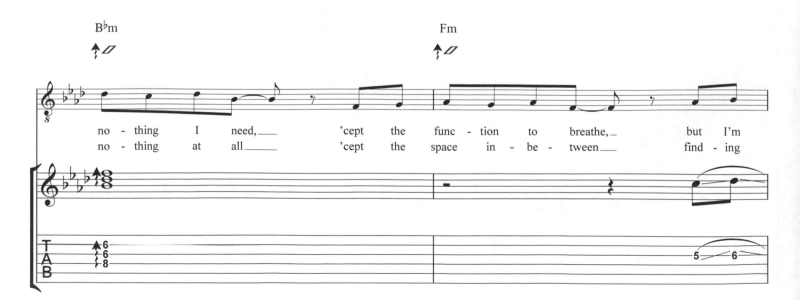

not real - ly fussed, ___ does-n't mat - ter to me. ___
out what you're called, ___ and re - peat - ing your name. ___

let ring - - - - - - - - - - - - - - - - - - -

Ru - by, Ru - by, Ru - by, Ru - by. ___ (Ah - ah - ah - ah - ah -

*Gtrs. 1+2 (elec.)

Chorus

*composite part

- ah.) ___ And do ya, do ya, do ya, do ya, ___ (Ah - ah - ah - ah - ah -

know what you're do - ing, do - ing to me?_____ (Ah - ah - ah - ah - ah -

-ah.)

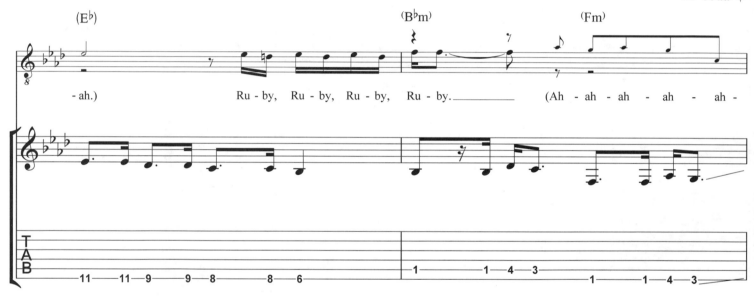

To Coda

-ah.)

Ru - by, Ru - by, Ru - by, Ru - by._____ (Ah - ah - ah - ah - ah -

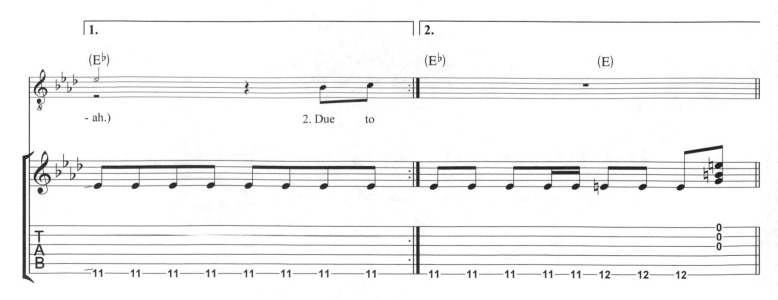

1.

2.

-ah.)

2. Due to

Bridge

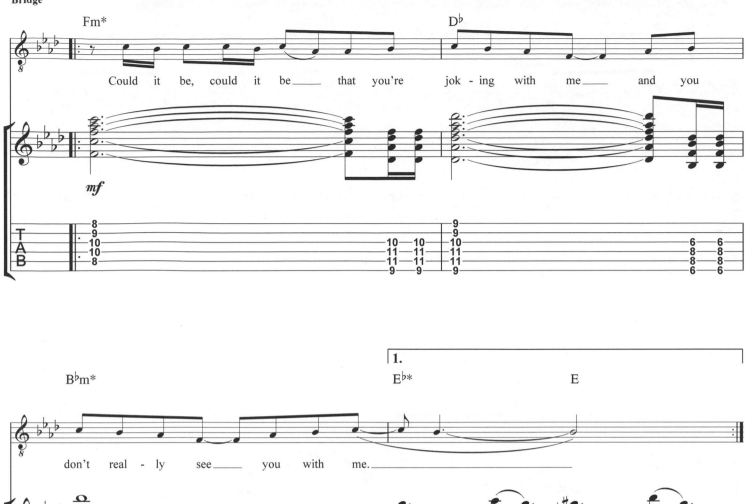

Could it be, could it be____ that you're jok-ing with me____ and you

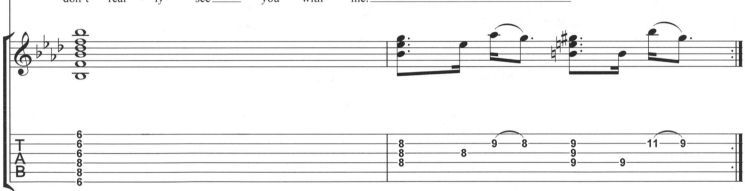

don't real-ly see____ you with me.____

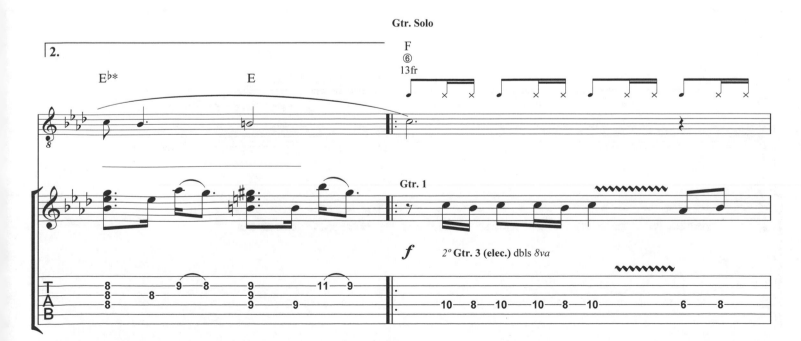

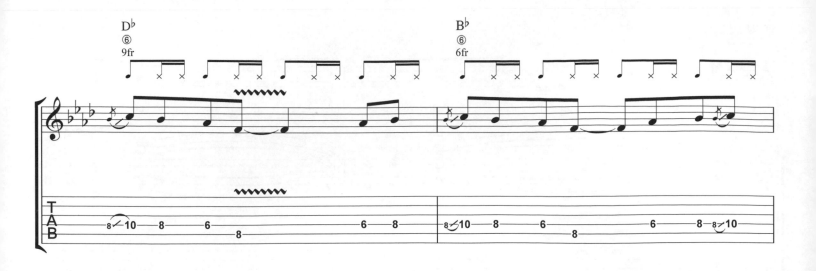

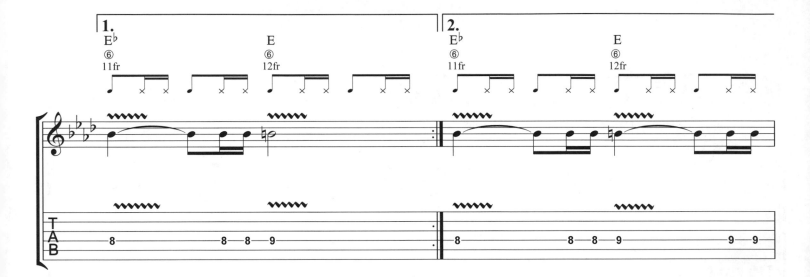

⊕ Coda

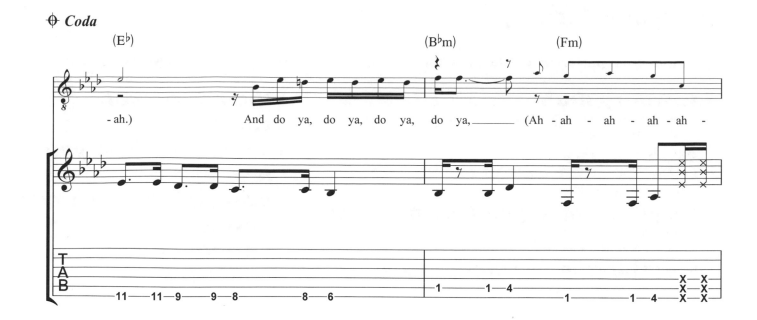

And do ya, do ya, do ya, do ya,_____ (Ah - ah - ah - ah - ah -

- ah.)
Da   da   da,_____   Da   da   da,_____   know   what   you're   do - ing,   do - ing

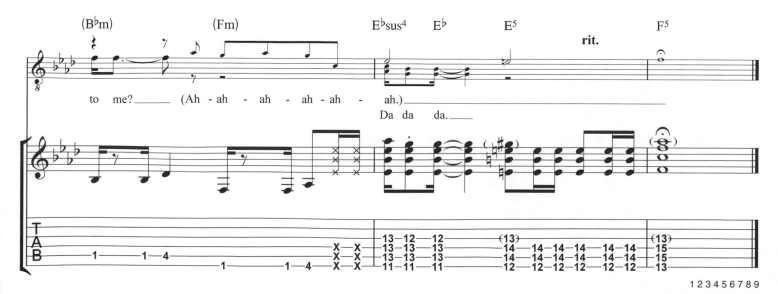

to   me?_____   (Ah - ah - ah - ah - ah -   ah.)
Da   da   da._____

1 2 3 4 5 6 7 8 9

CD track listing

full instrumental performances (with guitar)...

1 the angry mob
(Wilson/Hodgson/White/Rix/Baines)
Rondor Music (London) Limited.

2 caroline, yes
(Wilson/Hodgson/White/Rix/Baines)
Rondor Music (London) Limited.

3 everyday i love you less and less
(Wilson/Hodgson/White/Rix/Baines)
Rondor Music (London) Limited.

4 everything is average nowadays
(Wilson/Hodgson/White/Rix/Baines)
Rondor Music (London) Limited.

5 i predict a riot
(Wilson/Hodgson/White/Rix/Baines)
Rondor Music (London) Limited.

6 modern way
(Wilson/Hodgson/White/Rix/Baines)
Rondor Music (London) Limited.

7 oh my god
(Wilson/Hodgson/White/Rix/Baines)
Rondor Music (London) Limited.

8 ruby
(Wilson/Hodgson/White/Rix/Baines)
Rondor Music (London) Limited.

backing tracks only (without guitar)...

9 the angry mob
10 caroline, yes
11 everyday i love you less and less
12 everything is average nowadays
13 i predict a riot
14 modern way
15 oh my god
16 ruby

To remove your CD from the plastic sleeve,
lift the small lip to break the perforations.
Replace the disc after use for convenient storage.